Magic Mates
and the
Big Knickers Scandal

Jane West

Illustrated by

RISING★STARS

Rising Stars UK Ltd.
22 Grafton Street, London W1S 4EX
www.risingstars-uk.com

The right of Jane West to be identified as the author of this work
has been asserted by her in accordance with the Copyright, Design
and Patents Act 1988.

Published 2008

Cover design: Button plc
Illustrator: Stik, Bill Greenhead for Illustration
Text design and typesetting: Andy Wilson
Publisher: Gill Budgell
Editor: Jane Wood

British Library Cataloguing in Publication Data.
A CIP record for this book is available from the British Library

ISBN: 981 1 84680 331 4

Printed in the UK by CPI Bookmarque, Croydon, CR0 4TD

Mixed Sources
Product group from well-managed
forests and other controlled sources
www.fsc.org Cert no. TT-COC-002227
© 1996 Forest Stewardship Council

Contents

Meet the Magic Mates

**The Magic Mates are best friends –
but that doesn't mean they're all alike.**

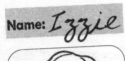

Name: *Izzie*

The sporty one: can climb trees, surf and take on the boys at their own game – and win.

Travels by: running!

Loves: trendy tracksuits, open skies and sandy beaches.

Hates: standing still.

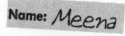

Name: *Meena*

The girly one: uses her mobile for networking and planning her social life.

Travels by: Mum's car (her personal chauffeur).

Loves: pink and her Magic Mates.

Hates: breaking a nail.

Name: Ginger

The ginger one: you don't wanna mess with this feisty gal – the Kung Fu and quick quip queen!

Travels by: push-scooter.

Loves: Jackie Chan and her Magic Mate pals.

Hates: nail extensions.

Name: Jo

The clever one: uses her brains and quick wit to talk her way out of trouble. Sometimes she's a bit too quick.

Travels by: bicycle and is designing a pair of motorised rollerblades.

Loves: Jacqueline Wilson, Cathy Cassidy and Albert Einstein.

Hates: being called 'geek', 'nerd', 'swot' or 'boffin'.

Name: 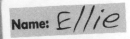 Ellie

The fashion-conscious one: can tell her Prada from her Asda and knows how to accessorise.

Travels by: limousine, of course! (But only in her dreams.)

Loves: shopping.

Hates: anything to do with getting dirty; anyone who upsets her Magic Mates.

Name: Yash

The funky punky one: the 'alternative' one of the gang who hugs trees, people and furry animals.

Travels by: skateboard.

Loves: having a good time.

Hates: bullies.

It's a Scandal!

Jo	There's been another washing line attack.
Ellie	How can you attack a washing line?
Ginger	Perhaps it's a Kung Fu washing line and it fought back!

Jo   Ha, ha. Very funny.
No, I mean some more clothes
have been stolen from
a washing line. It's in
the local paper.

Meena   Stealing clothes! That's terrible!

Izzie   Do they know who the thief is?

Jo   They haven't caught him yet –
          or her. But there's something
          odd about it all.

Ginger What's that?

Jo   The thief only steals knickers.

Yash   Knickers?

Jo   Yes. Big knickers.

Izzie   What do you mean?

Jo   The thief only steals big knickers
           from washing lines.
           Other clothes and small knickers
           aren't touched.

Meena Who'd want to do
           something like that?

Jo   I don't know. And the police
           don't know either.

Izzie   It is very odd.

Jo   There's something more to this,
             I'm sure of it.

Jo thinks it's a puzzle and Jo
is never wrong. Can the Magic Mates
catch the thief and give him
a dressing-down?

Jo   We should try to catch
          the thief red-handed.

Meena   Don't be silly.
          That would be dangerous.

Ginger Meena is right.
          That wouldn't be a good idea.

Jo   I don't mean try and stop him –
          or her – or anything like that.
          Just catch them in the act.

Ellie   Jo's got a plan, I can tell!

Jo   Yes, I have! We could set a trap.
              We could put some washing out
              and wait with a camera.
              When the thief comes,
              we could take a photograph
              and show it to the police.

Ginger   That's a great idea!

Jo   We could do it at my house.
           My mum is doing the washing
           today.

Izzie   Has she got some really
            big knickers?

Jo   No, but I can get some
            from my Gran. She won't mind.

The Magic Mates have a plan
to catch a thief!

Magic Mates
in Knicker Shocker Glory!

Izzic and Jo
set a trap to catch
the Big Knickers
Thief. They help
Jo's mum to do the washing.
Then they help her to peg it out
on the washing line.

Jo   I've got my camera ready.

Izzie We can hide behind the curtains.
The thief will never see us.

Jo Now all we have to do is wait.

Waiting for the thief is boring.
The girls take turns looking out
of the window. They feel very sleepy.
Jo wakes up suddenly.

Jo   Wait a minute!
The blue knickers have gone!

Izzie   How did that happen
without us seeing the thief?

Jo   I don't know.
He must have been really fast.

Izzie   I was watching the whole time.
Well, I only fell asleep
for a second. I didn't see anyone
in the garden, only your
black-and-white cat.

Jo   Hang on a minute.
What did you say?

Izzie   I said that I only saw your
black-and-white cat.

Jo   I haven't got a
black-and-white cat.
My cat is grey all over.
That's why we call her Smokey.

Izzie   Oh, well, I saw someone
              else's cat, then.

Jo   I wonder ...

Izzie   What are you thinking, Jo?

Jo is thinking hard. Izzie is bursting
with questions.

Jo   When our cat was getting ready
to have her kittens, she went all
over the house looking for a
good place. She chose the shed
in the garden because it's quiet.
I put a box in the shed, and lots
of old sheets and pillows.
She made a cosy nest and
had her kittens there.

Izzie   What's that got to do with
             the Big Knickers Thief?

Jo   What if the cat you saw
             is the thief?

Izzie   You mean the thief
             is a cat burglar?!

Jo   She might have been stealing
             clothes so she could make herself
             a nice warm place to have
             her kittens.

Jo   Look! The black-and-white cat
has come back. Let's see what
she does.

The black-and-white cat has a big
round tummy. It looks like she is
having kittens. The cat jumps up
and pulls another pair of big knickers
off the washing line and runs away
with them.

Jo Wow! Did you see that!
And I got a photo of it, too.
We've caught the Big Knickers
Thief red-handed ...
or red-pawed.

Izzie I'm glad your plan worked,
but I'm worried about that cat.
I don't think she's got
any owners. We must help her.

Jo   You're right. But first we have to
           find out where she's hiding.
           Let me think …

Izzie hopes that Jo has another good idea
because she's really worried about
the black-and-white cat.

Caught!
Cat Burglar has Kittens!

Jo and Izzie have to find where the black-and-white cat is hiding. They must hurry because the cat is going to have some kittens to look after, too.

Jo   I've got an idea. Look at this map of our town. If we put crosses where all the big knickers have been stolen, we will know where to look for the cat.

Izzie   That's a good idea.
She won't go far from her nest.
But there's one thing that
puzzles me. Why did the cat
only steal big knickers?

Jo   Well, I've been thinking
about that, too. When Smokey
had kittens, she wanted lots
of soft stuff to rest on.
I gave her old towels, pillows,
sheets – soft stuff like that.
Knickers are soft, too.

Izzie   Why only choose *big* knickers?

Jo   My guess is that big knickers
are easier for her to reach
'cos they're, well, big!

Jo and Izzie mark six places on the map.
All of them have had big knickers stolen.

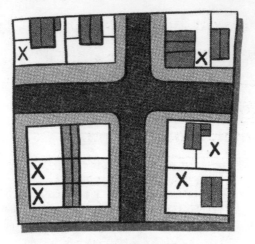

Izzie   Look! All the big knickers have been stolen from these four streets. I think the cat must be making her nest near here. But how will we find her?

Jo   She could be hiding in a garden shed or a garage. I know! I'll ask Mum if I can have some of that chicken left over from dinner. Cats love chicken!

Izzie   Good idea!

The girls walk up and down
the four streets. They call the cat
and wave the bits of chicken.
They hope that the cat will smell
the food and come running.

Jo   Here, kitty! Chicken!
              Yummy chicken!

Izzie   Here, puss! Dinner!
              Roast chicken!

An old lady sees them. She wonders what they're doing. She doesn't often see two girls walking up and down the street waving chicken drumsticks.

Old Lady Oh dear! Have you lost your cat?

Izzie She's not our cat, but we are worried about her.

Jo She's black and white. We think she might be having kittens. We want to help her.

Izzie   Have you seen
a black-and-white cat?

Old Lady Yes, I have! I saw her
in that garden over there.
The house is empty because
the people who lived there
moved away. I think they had
a black-and-white cat.

Izzie   Oh, poor cat! She must have
              got left behind when her owners
              moved away.

Jo   Let's go in the garden
              and look for her.

The two girls see a shed behind the house.
The door is open. They look inside.

There is the black-and-white cat,
in a nest of knickers. Next to her
are two tiny balls of fur.

Jo   Oh, look! We've found her!

Izzie   And her kittens.

Paws for Applause!

Jo and Izzie have found the cat burglar –
and her two kittens. Izzie phones the vet
and he comes to the house.

Vet   Well done, girls. The owners
were so sad and worried
when they couldn't find
their cat. I hoped we'd find her.

Izzie   Is she okay?

Vet   She's very hungry,
              but don't worry. She'll be fine,
              and so will her kittens.

Izzie   Do you know her name?

Vet   Yes. She's called Mrs Socks,
              because of her white paws.

Jo   Ha, ha, ha! Her name suits her!

Izzie   This kitten is all black,
but with white paws at the front.
We could call her 'Gloves'!

Jo   And this kitten is all white, but
         with black paws at the back.
         We could call him 'Boots'!

Vet   Boots, Gloves and Mrs Socks.
         It's almost a whole wardrobe!

Jo   And don't forget
         all the Big Knickers, too!

The SOL

30p

MRS SOCKS IN BIG KNICKER SCANDAL
– CAT BURGLAR CAUGHT!

About the Author

Jane West doesn't have a cat, but she has got a dog called Pip. He has been microchipped by a vet. If he ever gets lost, like Mrs Socks, a vet could find his owner from the microchip. And that would be another happy ending!

Jane West:

- lives by the beach in Cornwall
- likes taking Pip paddling in the sea
- has worked in an art gallery, a bookshop and a school.

Now she's a writer, and has had great fun writing about the Magic Mates. She hopes you liked reading about them.

Famous Cats

The Aristocats

Have you seen this cartoon
film? It's about a family
of aristocratic (very posh)
cats. An alley cat helps
to stop an evil servant
from kidnapping them.

The Cat in the Hat

Did you read this book when you were little?
It's by Dr Seuss, and is written in rhyme.

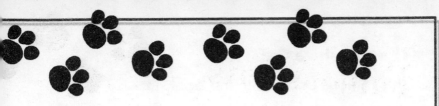

Bastet

Bastet is an Egyptian cat-goddess.
People worshipped her 5000 years ago.
She's the daughter of the sun-god Ra
and the protector of women and children.
She has the body of a woman and the head
of a cat.

Cait Sith

Cait Sith is a fierce fairy cat from Scotland.
It is black with a white spot on its chest.
Some say Cait Sith used to be a witch!

The Cheshire Cat

This famous cat is from the book
Alice in Wonderland by Lewis Carroll.
The Cheshire Cat can turn himself invisible.
His smile is the last thing to disappear!

The Mousehole Cat

This is a lovely story by Antonia Barber.
It has wonderful pictures by Nicola Bayley.
It's about a cat who saves the people
of Mousehole from hunger. And yes,
Mousehole is a real place! It's in Cornwall.
You say it so it sounds like 'Muzzel'.

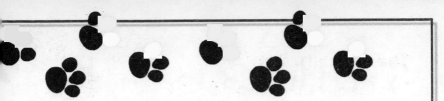

Cat Woman

Cat Woman is a baddie in the Batman films. Okay, she's not really a cat, but she is a bit cat-like. And she likes to drink milk!

Garfield

Garfield is a famous cartoon cat.
You can find out all about him
on his website:
www.garfield.com

Grimalkin

You don't want to get on the wrong side
of this cat! He belongs to three evil witches
in Shakespeare's play *Macbeth*.

There are lots of fun facts about cats
on this website:
www.moggies.co.uk

The Things People Say!

'It is a very inconvenient habit
of kittens that what ever you say to them,
they always purr.'

Lewis Carroll,
author of Alice in Wonderland

'Cats are a mysterious kind of folk.
There is more passing in their minds
than we are aware of.'

Sir Walter Scott, writer

'Thousands of years ago, cats were worshipped
as gods. Cats have never forgotten this.'

We don't know who wrote this.
What do you think they meant?

Joke Time

Did you hear about the cat who swallowed a ball of wool? She had mittens!

Izzie What do you get when you cross an elephant with a cat?

Jo A big furry creature that purrs while it sits on your lap and squashes you.

Jo What is a cat's favourite colour?

Izzie Purrrrrrrple!

Izzie Why did the cat run away from the tree?

Jo Because it was afraid of the bark!

Quiz

1 Why should you microchip your pet cat?

2 Would a cat ever live in a mouse hole?

3 Are there any cats in the Batman films?

4 Would Cait Sith make a good pet?

5 What magic can the Cheshire Cat do?

Answers

1 To help you find them if they get lost.
2 Yes! There's a place in Cornwall called Mousehole. It's where the Mousehole Cat lives.
3 No. Just Cat Woman, and she's a woman, not a cat.
4 No! It's a fierce fairy cat who used to be a witch!
5 He can turn invisible.

How did you score?

0–1 Have you been catnapping?

2–3 I think you made a few mice-takes!

4–5 Purrrfect!

Magic Mates

RISING ★ STARS